UNPROTECTED
LEXICON

alexa chrisbacher

Cover design by **Jensen Keller**

Cover photography by **Case Chrisbacher**

Portions of this book use interpolations of **"The Riot Grrl Manifesto"** originally published in *Bikini Kill Zine 2*

1.

We were born on a hot track in Texas, of dust and sweat pooling on the

lines. Descendants of cutoff jeans and pierced nostrils, stick-and-poke,

cassette tapes, and Manic Panic. Skaters in shades of Electric Lizard or

Mystic Heather.

Moving in circles, passing a pair of scissors, tape, glue to the left.

Sharpie articles of high priestesses, a blood oath of menstruation,

calling for true-punkrock-soul-crusaders to start bands in garages, join a

local roller derby league, write letters to senators or Joan of Arc, Make.

New. Sex. Positions. name our pussies after dead poets.

This is sanctuary.

2.

Early summer heat: women fly by in fishnets and skirts. They have

rockstar names, short haircuts and tattoos, they have grit and girlfriends

in punk bands. She wants to be like them. Fearless.

To imagine wheels under her feet and stumble in subconscious, unable

to overlap their images with hers. The story she tells herself about

herself.

Lex dreams of *her*, being with her. Dreams of herself, of becoming.

Unfolds

in numberless selves. We dream of a chrysalis where we sleep until it's

time to meet the outside world, wild with fearful beasts.

She dreams she is fast, watching screaming faces through the

plexiglass of a converted hockey rink. Skating past a high school teacher with sweaty hands and an open zipper. Thoughts that she is too

something. Billboards big and airbrushed stretched over the interstate.

A scale, hospital room, prom dress, term paper.

She remembers people who label things: good/bad; right/wrong;

sin/self,

who abandon, who hurt, people who say you can't be anything but what

you already are.

Vibrating forms toss teeth at the infield and screech like car brakes.

But they can't reach Lex from the sidelines where she left them,

gnashing

behind the barrier. All they can do is watch us, on skates. Surfacing.

She's awake. We write a new story to tell about ourselves.

3.

A poet starts a band, when she walks the revolution's coming. Kathleen

Hanna leaps into the crowd at her shows to throw out hecklers. Jarring

masculinity. She sends spells into the future, a seance with our

godmothers in Austin.

Call girls to the front. Her manifesto becomes sport.

BECAUSE we don't want to assimilate to someone else's

(boy) standards of what is or isn't.

BECAUSE I believe with my wholeheartmindbody that girls are a force

that will change the world.

Mic feedback and torn denim. They meet at Casino el Camino near a jukebox. A man named Devil Dan sells a rockabilly brawl to a crowd of

women.

He hands out flyers. He wants them. He wants a circus with roller

skates

bare tits and bandanas, bears on unicycles country music lipstick rings

of fire.

"It's babes beating each other up," he says.

Our godmothers dig the idea but hate The Devil and run him out of

town.

BECAUSE we must take over the means of production to create our

own moanings.

A manifesto becomes bylaws to shape their chaos. Riot grrrls step onto

the street, now Texas Roller Girls. Rebel girl, can you hear it?

Another call to the front.

By the skaters for the skaters. Fuck the bar. Fight the dullness of shit

society.

4.

For one hundred and twenty seconds count a pair of stars and two pivot

stripes. Opposing teams made of five skaters, ten in total. Behind a line

two jammers in starred helmets wait for five seconds to pass, wait to fly

or collide.

Blockers bend at knees and waists, create a human wall.

Break a seam open and eat what's inside, charge through open lanes,

embody defiance.

Lex learns to live forever. In two-minute increments. An all and nothing

at once interpretation of fracture or undefined threshold. Our hair hangs

long and wild down backs, sheared at the jaw, or shaved smooth to the

scalp.

From our laundry lines hang leather catsuits and pantyhose, capes,

bloomers, chest binders, nipple tassels, rusting armor, and fishnet

stockings.

The skaters who have moved across this ground are still here, soaked

into the worn acrylic floor, perched on the wooden beams overhead,

leaning against the home team bench with hands cupped around open

mouths. We hang empty helmets from the rafters. A spectral lineage.

Not all our friends speak in words.

You may leave derby, but you never quite leave it behind. It marks you.

It soaks into your bones, sometimes so deeply they fracture and spill

marrow onto muscle tissue. The sport settles in the creases of your

knuckles and stains your biceps like permanent marker from last night's

scrimmage.

A one and a zero still faint across pale,

tattooed skin.

Wheels and fingernails press into your thighs, into your sense of self.

Scar, bruise, surgical steel beneath the skin. A freedom of revolutions,

speed and endless track. Eternal collapsing and rebuilding.

Orion's belt is on her forearm, three round marks of similar shape size

and hue. They are a brief history of another's grip, of a temporary

human structure where hands flat on shoulders and palms pushing

chests form links and we are geometric, a flexing of flesh and angles

and bones merging, shouting vulnerability and grit in unison, catching a

jammer, absorbing impact to ribs and backs and chests.

Bodies cracked and bolted breaking on each other perpetually.

Her form becomes a map of contact each night. Impact restructuring her

cells from the surface, down. As Lex peels away clothing, she faces the

bathroom mirror and studies constellations that change shades, shift

shapes and spread across her forearms and back. Anatomy bearing

marks in maroon and green, marks of brutality, black and violet.

An identity pressed into her, a tiny trauma of proud fascia.

5.

Where will flesh end and ideas begin? I am made by contact,

our combined context.

In the shower she counts them, categorizes and names them *bruise*,

drawing dotted lines from one to another until she finds proof of shape.

Proof that she's really here, that her body is actually her own.

Hit me, Lex says. *Push me, knock me to the floor. I am tough enough to*

do this. This is a real body, without editing / tethered to a specific

moment in time.

I am able.

Seen, when her hair is long. A figure full of milk, hips the contour of a

language. Memory of something ancient and maternal. A name, an

illusion. She

is seen shimmering truth untouchable like mirage heat. Question

unanswered, femme magic.

She is heard, with head shaved. Masculine tongue flip, queer footsteps.

Earthy tones, husky and sweet. Turning of soil. An earring and middle

finger. Heard, a crackle of fire and sage. Whoosh thump. Pop.

Lex is a universe, she is container. Expansive condensation, multiple.

Wet. Invisible in lack of shape / slash of category. She is most

understood when fingertips touch lips and nape of neck, twisted wicks and wax slide down a thigh. Essence of a pulse, wing beat flutter, pearl

and petal.

Cartographical study of another night's practice:

She sheds an old structure. Building a new shape. Soaks the bruises in

steam and watches soapy water pull disposable parts toward the drain,

another circle another layer washed away.

6.

"Start a band. If you want people to hear what you're doing, don't do

spoken word. No one likes spoken word."

Kathy Acker is sighing advice into a tepid cup of hibiscus tea. Stirring. A

teenage poet spreads the advice across toast and bites. This *super hot*

chick, posing as a journalist. She chews. Where do you go if you want

to make change? 1990's Washington. A good place to start. Evergreen

State College. A stage or a coffee shop or a writers retreat. Fuck the

coffee shop. Start a—

Band together, a new wave. Don't make poems birth manifestos, write

down your demands and eat them onstage, spew them back into a screaming crowd of men with closed fists asking where the real music is

who gave guitars to chicks

                                                    what the hell is Bikini Kill?

Call to the girls in the room, this is for them.

Incite a riot.

Bring the girls to the front.

Uncle Leon and the Alibis ask, "Will roller derby save your soul?" A track can hold us all. *This is our world.* We dismantle boundaries in

locker rooms and bar patios, restructure countries kneeling for anthems.

Local and international, a re-united nations. Taped track lines are

borders we will keep. Blue postcards from Australia. Wave hello from

Rose City, Angel City, Rage City.

We inherit punk rock and riot grrrl and speak with Marxian tongues.

Stomp your feet on the ground in unison.

The anger of women is important and valid.

The anger of women is messy. It ricochets everywhere and gets all over

everything, pierces the shoulder of a bystander, splatters across cheeks

like paint leaving a brush. Staining. Ruining.

The anger of women looks you in the eye, unwavering, accusing.

This is sisterhood this is sport this is revolution.

And it's everywhere.

It's a dance,

a performance on eight wheels. Jammers

spin in stars, leaping above a crowded room, torsos twisting and juke

partners colliding beneath tangled strings of light. Thin dust underneath

seeps through cracks, rising in waves with every back that hits the

ground, with every fragment of a larger impact, a swirl twisting in on

itself.

We are in a Barn, our own place of worship, lined with old church pews

propped up by stacks of bricks and wooden crates and here, here we

find our real names.

Behind the crimped bay doors we are far away from what we have

been,

what we have been called. We are *other* / we are alter ego. Identity is

more than a reflection of others onto you. We tongue expectation like a

mouthguard

across our teeth. It's the freedom of moving in a circle where you meet

yourself.

We are not born, we are made. Patched by x's of duct tape and

bandaids, a soma earned, built of pure fucking will.

Maybe you're rocking a baby to sleep while writing a dissertation,

stacking hay on a pig farm, or stuffing arepas in the back of a humid

food truck. Maybe you're reading a new recruit night flyer for your local

roller derby league.

The clack of roller skates on hardwood, tear of velcro yanked apart,

knuckles popped on the bench between jams, a starting whistle and

swelling shouts from the crowd. You are part of it.

7.

Wear Doc Martens and aquamarine in your hair.

Vote.

Discuss racism / womanhood / money / transphobia / queer sex /

patriarchy / homophobia

out loud,

in public places.

Pray to Texas Roller Girls, Saint Margaret, and Legba the god of words.

Claim your space. *She wants everything.*

Recite Kathy Acker loudly in a crowd. And write. *Writing,* she says,

especially fiction, is magic. This is not fiction, my friends, but it is magic

nonetheless. Send words from Then to Now,

hoping they'll wash up on an island's shore or slide through the space

under a bedroom door. Poems for Nefertiti penciled on paper lanterns, a take-out menu scrawled with questions for Eleanor Roosevelt, elegy for

Zsa Zsa Gabor whispered into open palms.

Lie awake under a full moon with amethyst under your tongue. Clutch a

vibrating wand and cast spells with your orgasm.

Seal erotic couplets in Corona bottles and toss them out to sea.

8.

We slouch against a pool table on a day just like any other day,

swinging our political clout like bare breasts or chalked cues or

autonomy.

Maybe you have to create. A self. Catch a reflection in the dingy 7-11

window. Is that what we're all doing here? Making an identity and

drinking shitty coffee. Not given _____ . Why we buy skates and girl-punk tapes and date our friends and write poetry and hope for

something more interesting than what we're told we deserve?

Dear Lex, we need you when:

the world tumbles backward and we are moving out or coming out or

spinning out in a crowded bar / our mothers commit suicide and bosses

spit diluted tobacco into styrofoam cups saying it's better to marry for

money

/ we're the wrong shape or size wanting to shrink to the width of our

bones, gauzy and smooth like /

They know who we are now, a swarm of impending change, misandrist

monsters trying to take the Christ out of xmas. Lesbians with hairy

armpits and neck tattoos. We're shaving our heads in internet chatrooms, crying in public, and ordering sex toys on Amazon during

our lunch break.

BECAUSE we need to encourage and be encouraged in the face of our

own insecurities.

We vote / get abortions / watch porn / get married / get divorced / we

die.

Just like you, Lex.

Imagine walking down the street in any outfit you choose because

there's no whistle from the corner, no sharp car keys sticking out from

between your fingers, no pepper spray shaped like a tube of lipstick, no advice from older sisters about how to escape a stranger on foot or

keep *an incident* quiet at school. But

Acker says no one's here to help us.

It's time to help each other.

BECAUSE we are angry at a society that tells us Girl = Dumb, Girl =

Bad, Girl = Weak.

Hear the lie (there's no problem anymore—-it was taken care of in the

60s or on social media, by Oprah or after the ninetieth amendment or

something.)

Don't believe it.

We only have each other.

9.

Lex writes poetry that holds breath / turns blue,

blackened heart, cheeks, toes. Swelling bodies and verse, sweeping

lines—

    extract it, a kind of wringing out. Soon she will be empty.

Closed doors and a cheap coffee pot, meandering containment,

non-object loss.

She doesn't think of it often but if she closes her eyes and tries really

hard

Lex can go back there, feel it, like biting down hard on an aching tooth.

Just to see if the nerves will spark.

Woman wrapped in sheets, a failed transformation. Insides unchanged

exterior blown open. Floating shreds post-apocalyptic ash.

Some days Lex feels it too. The sinking. She looks out the window of a

city bus at nothing and feels the space inside her. An empty swell,

heavy. Vast starlessness in her chest. Her palms sweat to consider

relief.

She folds the sinking in half, and in half again. Creases it smaller

and thicker, but easier to hold. Crushing the echoes to a size she can

stash away. Forget about.

Grief adorns memory like sunspots overlapping the familiar. Pile of

laundry or car door quickens pulse. Bright second of violence.

Who are we when the wake ends?

Her mother and a plastic bag, unceremonious exit. She'll tell Kathy

about it sometime. They have this in common.

10.

There's a girl in gold. Lex seals herself into that day, the first time she

wore roller skates / the first time she saw *her*. Tequila in a garage,

scattered motorcycle parts and crushed beer cans from a party the night

before. They play their favorite songs from 15 years ago through a tinny,

portable speaker.

Have you met your Bobbi Trout? A riot grrrl or leaping skater in white

skates,

a spunky flygirl sucking big fat cigars with Amelia Earhart. She's blowing

smoke rings in the faces of sweaty reporters, uniform wrinkled and

cuffed at

the ankle, a vision smeared in grease. Pariah. Pretending to masturbate

the handle of a wrench.

A marked surface. Fluid beneath the skin, blue-black or crimson like

heritage. *Hallmark of outlaw, desolate desert-born*. Designating realms

beyond.

Have you met Speedlejuice? Icon of power. Marked, in men's clothes

with a ring in her mouth.

Whiskey-born, an odd girl. Should we call this what it is?

She told Marlene Dietrich to start wearing slacks and broke a flying

record all in an afternoon. Cut the track and crossed lines. *Those rules*

are for someone else, baby.

Maybe she's the hero of this story, the heretic. Proud of her difference.

A composition of *other,* a person in flux escaping to the sky, barrel

rolling over the Heartland with a map in her back pocket. Skating feels

like flying.

Lex sips a gin and tonic with Amelia, presses the toe of her boot into an

ankle under the table, and asks why she disappeared.

We lean on a bar top with Gertrude Stein and swat at gossip about

whose lipstick is smeared on another's neck. Call our plays from the

bench, dance slow and close with an heiress, an actress in a press-on

mustache, a bus mechanic in blood red stilettos.

They get drunk and fuck in suspension. A safety in mitosis, wrapped

with blankets, walls of each other/ their cells, underside of a leaf. Here

on a teammate's couch, a basement, backseat. Hidden away in quiet

moments, when

no one would notice hands down another's pants because they are learning a language like brail. Waiting for their season of emergence.

Mapping a lexicon.

Lex had loved women before but only from afar only in her head lightly

tethered to her heart, feelings blushing at the ends of fingers creating a

closed circuit of a body at the clit. She runs her hands down and across, tastes lips and elbow creases, inhales them into the space behind her

eyes where they live, but never for long. Not like this,

not like lavender mist rising in the periphery.

Not like

After party. Snow flurries in an empty parking lot, suppose she were to

kiss Juice. Swallow her whole. Run to her warm center and lay down.

Rest.

Frosted breath. Bow tie. Heels. Saddle shoes and guilt. Souls soaked

in_____. Remember the gold helmet, the gym where they learned how

to. Move. Closer to a still(ed) image.

But, she's never. They have a _____ . Is this, _____ ? What are

they? A game of seconds.

Her pillows smell like hair after she leaves and Lex is always tired

without. She wants to sleep forever on the scent of her head. Write

ballads on the lines the sheets leave on a cheek and ask, are you warm

enough? (Am I enough?)

Bobbi reels off a string of four-letter words for the fainting press. Bobbi

takes a gulp from a flask in her pants pocket. We hold fingers to our

mouths in the shape of a V and flick our tongues between them. She is

a blurring of something, neither/both, is permission. Because she is

_____ ,

we can be anything.

11.

She deserves this as much as the figurines on a tiered vanilla cake.

Juice and Lex. Beads of oil in a warm bath. Do you remember dancing

in late snow outside the bar? A white balloon tangles on the power line.

Lex feels swollen on certain streets, in her room, walking through the

market. Clumsy, or this t-shirt is too tight. Bleached teeth and mascara

in a high school bedroom. Taking Juice's pants off on a pullout couch.

Catching the corner of a door frame. An indigo dress hangs in a closet

for Thanksgiving with her

grandparents. *Are you seeing anyone these days? Don't worry, one day*

you'll meet a man who will change your mind.

Lex feels visible from very far away.

In an empty and dry place, there is no name for what she is, *queer*.

There's no word on the family mantle for a love like aperture. Eyes like

Arizona.

An expansive, delicate spreading. There are plenty of words for what

she's not, for poured concrete and mortar. Can you stand on both sides

of a wall? Starved for language.

The history of words falls short of a safe grammar, short of self. What

would we be called? A Macrosoma soul, perched on a windowsill, if she

were named divine—

12.

Joan of Arc and Kathy Acker play poker in the summer heat. Acker

explains genital piercing over a straight flush. She's winning. Legba is

better at cards than the Archangel Michael. The poet and heretic have similar hairstyles, but one recently doused hers in peroxide to melt the

natural color out. We can't tell them apart.

Joan says she is whoever the saints say she is, savior. Acker says

when you ride a motorcycle with a labia piercing, the little bead on the

ring acts like a vibrator. The body becomes a self-contained object of

pleasure. As ordained.

The god of words is a catalyst for the spirit who speaks through her. A carved candle. Red of flames red of hair, the heat of everything that's

happened so far. Waiting to be lit.

Is identity what others have decided on your behalf? A red name tag

with a symbol in the blank space. *Hello, my name is:*

Now we know what you are.

Show plagiarism in self portraits. The absence of words is the absence

of intimacy. Lex touches her chest where she stores shed eyelashes and morning exhales, an edifice of collar bone and sternum to hold the

sense of someone.

Struggle with unanticipated shift. Her father made a shape of her before

she. Became wind. *I'm dating a woman*. There's a neck brace supporting his spine and he can't look anywhere but back at her face.

Sedimentary rock erodes

into arch. Not what they. Predicted, apologize but. Her father loves her,

he says. She is storm. He asks for words, a comma or phrase. She

gives him sand.

Both here, at this table, they move forward to learn a new landscape.

Something vast and undefined and startling and

Pray to poet and heretic for the language of spectrum. Watch love hues,

shadows cast across tile.

All we know is what we have words for.

13.

There is a constant state of fracture behind the walls of the Barn. A

healing frame for the internal, ribs or beams and splintered walls. We are the pumping blood of this body and we sacrifice the salt of

ourselves.

Our Barn is layered like we are, flesh and form, a pulse of people swirls

inside. Light spills from its mouth.

We are pupae in chrysós cathedrals. A stratum of holy viscera. Golden metamorphosis, hanging like bells from embodied domes. Practice

merging,

a transition.

A living whip, human wall, link and brace. Pain pressing against

pleasure.

An anatomy of four corners, connection to an inside and outside pedal

edge, like foundation. Feet, a base. Place of strength and balance with

lightness in the arches and flexibility through the toes. Wheels, an

extension. Engaging with an edge tilts the skate, challenges a direction,

creates a turn.

We embody spectrum. Cut away what doesn't fit, until we find our

shape.

Visible in public now, it still feels like a secret is cupped in their palms.

It's different with her, this reaching this horizontal spreading. It's not a

name or the timbre of her voice. We are back-to-back, hands out,

protecting each other

from the fragments of overheard conversations about. People like us.

Lex will inhabit her own interior, owning. Swelling from the inside out.

Ideas emotions textures, answering the call to incite.

A riot. It's not a new wave it's just.

You and me.

Edges grow in number and potential, multiplied by the infinite

conversations between ankle sinew, ligature, and muscle. Each stride plots points on a chart, through space—a spirograph of expendable

acceleration. Ahead, watch possibility divide and split, carve out a path

with the outer sharpness of a heel, the front arch of a foot, a plane

running along the toes.

Lex feels safe. Seen, not looked at. Encased in silk. Hardening.

Juice begins a line with words Lex knows, she builds an adverb for

Juice's actions. They feather metaphors for how their feelings spin fiber

around them. They aren't radical—just understood—and they can rest and read and fill in the blanks beneath tangled sheets and the *X-Files*

poster tacked to a ceiling.

Center of weight sits deep below the facia on smooth organ tissue.

Skater carries truth below the surface. A scarlet ball drops from the

chest to hips' cradle, rolling over one leg or another as they sink into a

turn or engrave the shape of their momentum into undefined space.

We find in our edge(s) an untethered place of control, a hard stop or

sweeping curve, a lift and swing. The body shifts along the motion,

rearranging itself to accommodate nuanced inertia. Corners of skin and

skeleton hold balance in motion, support the ankles and hold up the

arch. A reaction to the flick and press of internalized choreography. A

dance composed through violent collaboration.

14.

Cherry bomb, polymorphic poprock aesthetic of sharp saccharine *other.*

Queer athletes with jagged bangs, bright lipstick, and bandanas /

studded belts, shaved heads, bare faces / collage of safety pins and

resistance.

Externalizing rebel spirit.

Dozens spin and shatter in camera flash, torn skirts over fishnets

unravelling at the hem. Mouth guard, knee pads, crosshatched velcro

abrasions. Like aposematic spangles and tiger-stripes. Pocket Rocket,

Catastrophoebe,

Kid Vicious. Bright and lethal like unpalatable female butterflies.

We are sex symbols and dirty jokes, rockstars and onomatopoeia.

Choose a name and plot your metamorphosis. Superheroes with secret

identities stashed away in beige afternoon. A constant state of emerging

from metropolis phone booths, splintered plywood and golden ribs.

Writing our own stories of kindergarten teacher / nurse / attorney-by-

day,

                                                    Hero by night.

Stomp of boots in Austin, rally cry of leather and contusion. The

eyespots of a speckled wood distract attacking predators. We melt into

pseudonym, personify blur. We can still fly with a damaged wing.

We are superheroes and rockstars more than Jordan or Sydney or

Cody.

Cut-ups, stapled and pasted together, DIY people. The derby name

feels more real than the given name.

When catcalls make the back of your neck feel hot, remember you can

fly. You can leap over another skater with three seconds left in the jam.

This sport is living, in flux as rules are broken and shaped. Modifying

boundaries, evolving strategy. Nerves. Ritual, face paint and rock music

/

candy, meditation, and warm water / an application of uniform from the

feet up / screams in a dark room. A poem formed in preparation.

Static smooths into mental silence when wheel grooves make friction.

Heartbeat. Shouting fans sound far away, like noise from a memory. Or

a dream.

Feel. Fingertips resting on a teammate's thigh, lips pressed on a mouth

guard, an ankle brace beneath wool sock. Atmosphere holds weight

across shoulders and one thought remains:

Stop the jammer.

Girls spattered in blood, dresses cut short, mouths with thunder clap

voices offer silver fillings to the sky. Joan of Arc wore her soldier's

clothes off the battlefield, refusing

to split herself in two. On horseback in her fabled white armor of

hammered sun, polished halo of sainthood. So be: author, serial killer,

natural disaster, savior, or subversion. Whatever you want. Alter ego is

more real than secret identity. We are not fractions of anything, but all of

everything.

When the walls feel too close together and lights dim, realize you are

bigger than just you now. There is a team behind you, flygirls and

avengers. You will never be alone in battle again.

Who are you despite the scrubs or overalls? We don't have to accept

the names we are given. Crammed on a bench between motorcycle

mechanic and puzzle maker, shout wildly into the cacophony. This is

the shape you will become.

Paint your face, put on a uniform, go to war.

15.

We are intersection. Told to be, overlapping stories manifested; an up

and down sewn to left and right. At the y-axis we are called inheritance

and helix, hair texture, language and religion, spiral ladders to our given

names.

When we leave the Barn we feel out of context, identity is half what we

tell others about ourselves. What do we look like to the people at the

next table, the man who walked over to say,

I don't usually like short hair, but I'm willing to make an exception.

Identity is half what we tell ourselves. Reel in the impact. After-practice

beers only hold the stiffness off for an hour or so.

We are rescuing each other. Saviors. From ticker tape newsreels on the

mounted bar t.v. or dark alleyways, falling train cars, and politics of the

body. No one can wear a cape all the time.

Lex is blue collar New Jersey and Sonoran Desert saguaro. Mother's

hands and father's eyes. But, we cannot all be contained

                    in the up and down, so we spread out,

across space horizontally. They say straight parents make gay babies—

but queerness cannot stack on religion or eye color.

Formless, we spin silk buttons. Touch others. Find monoplanes, roller

rinks, and writers' circles.

Shove our way through life. *We don't hate, understand, we have to get*

back. The contact feels safe. *Fight the dullness of shit society.*

You can hit with a shoulder, a hip, a thigh.

Rest in the cool shadow of Bobbi Trout and Kathleen Hanna and Suzy

Hotrod. Lex's mother is a bathrobe on a hook now, sheen of urethane

wheels, tickets to the show tonight —

                                                        will you be there?

Building block person, living collage of aunts and teammates and

Kathy/Joan/Amelia. As big as history, absent and everywhere. Reliable,

yes

                                                        like

atmosphere.

In her arms Lex holds them. Women who survive. Flourish. Fractured

nose blood blooms down the pinks of their smiling gums, unexiting.

 Get on the track. Claim space. These skaters are feedback of creation

and destruction, reflective surface, wooden stools.

Hit me as hard as you can.

Lex peers though the plexiglass and catches a glimpse of herself,

obscured by flashing lights and thunder of pad, plastic, and concrete,

blending into other skaters, reshaping. Telling a new story.

16.

She is (this) today and tomorrow and yesterday, Lex is eye contact and

other, always making her own acquaintance. New to herself all the time.

She's learning about love like two mirrors facing each other.

Fingerprints and soap scum. Cloudy exhale. Her face soaks into itself

and she turns, an echo into her own image forever.

Write intimacy on the floor with our feet, supported by the rules we

create in this space. She turns and glides in acceptance, community.

Through the chink we try to make in expectations, how to move, shape

of a _____ , list of things Lex is not.

Where she stands, in the room and behind the glass all at once.

Undefined and unlocated. Spacial contradiction. We are safe here, in

praxis, realizing what it's like to see and be seen, syllables sucked from

sound. Stripped in honesty.

She was at odds with this body. Shamed for its hunger, its vulnerability

to words and laws and dress-shopping and slut-shaming and media and

menstruation and politics and self. But we don't have to be who we were

before. We are the careening of days around an apex,

counterclockwise. Why have we always thought this shape was so

important? Or time, so linear.

Lex learns about how fast she can move, how hard she can be hit and

still get back up. Constructing boundaries around the letters in her

name. There is a

space to fill, the gap between two others in a braced wall, a shoulder tucked into another's ribs, a half-time huddle, drops of sweat spreading

on the ground.

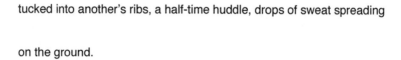

Bearings creak, summer heat rises from the floor. We are breath.

Sharp whistle and two skaters rush toward the pack, fisted hands and

pumping legs. Tensing against the impact, a lattice of limbs. Moving

lateral, low. Referees orbit the pack in full gear, calling penalties with

sweeping bows.

Push. Skate with shoulders forward like wading through thick space —

searching for a clearing. Manipulate weight. Escape.

Blockers absorb a hit into muscle tissue, sinking to ground another's

momentum. Jammers thrash in the seams, living fissure, incipient

space, just inches, the width of a toe stop is all they need. Blockers

predict a next step, turn, or leap. Juke to the left, jump the apex, grab

the arm of a teammate,

take a whip.

Get out like surfacing from deep water, a gasp and glance behind you.

It takes less than ten seconds for a jammer to circle the track and return

to the chaos of the pack.

A game of seconds.

Hundreds of blue plastic squares snap together and smooth rough

plywood,

a slanted circle of rope under wide yellow tape keeps us. Underneath, a

wooden skeleton of beams and boards, sawed and hammered into

place by our own hands. We are splintered and built back up.

Beneath, earth. An elemental blessing of dust shifting beneath the

surface. In our efforts, we make mud.

We know where we come from.

17.

This is a grasping.

18.

The world dictates a performance. To survive is to follow the

choreography. Can heroes fall in love?

We are at war with culture, heretics like Joan of Arc. Praying for an

answer to *what are you?* Not *what* but *who* reluctant to their prodding.

There is no word

for this, weapons cast aside with longing for open battle fields and a

lance from childhood. Remember your horse's name.

(Dear Voices, what am I? Soft pelvis cradle, hands holding another's

crown?

                                        Comprised secret.)

Breaking step. A hundred years raging through time and space find me.

Lex is linked by lifetimes and stars.

In a Barn on a pair of skates. On a stage we scream into a microphone.

Hold signs of cardboard and paint on a street corner in Seattle. Turn to

mist

in the cockpit of a small plane.

Queer in our armor, we fly strange flags. Peel apart a pronoun. Live in

liminal space between

masc u line and fem i nine.

Transgression in uniform. Unwilling to shed our armor off the battlefield.

Her hair is short now, and she is brave.

This isn't a war. It's a romance. Where is love in this abundance of

people.

The violence of people. What is our relationship to relationships but this

skin.

Lex and Juice crawl through a fissure to lay on a quilt. Of time. Sit in a

house made from the melted gold of her grandmother's wedding band,

a broken guitar string, discarded holiness. Dangling their feet off a ledge

of history. They dig into each other into the past into the real. Paring the

world from each other's backs in soft ribbons. Like shedding sunburned

skin.

Seep truth through pores and wonder if the structure is sound enough.

Joan, so strange, exhumed in a puritanical crusade and Mouseketeered

by

the West. Maid of Heaven. Unwilling symbol of abstinence.

We meet on charred ground, speak a language of colliding. Wield words

like swords.

There is a splitting, an opening. We show the tenderness of our

tongues.

Is it true that sex and violence are related?

Lex can see smoke in the distance. Damp beer bottles pop open and

Juice's face glows in the light of a bonfire. There's a shout, faraway

hooves clack on the ground. Banners of Then and Now, closing in.

19.

Amelia walks through men's spaces, seen. Transgressing with each

heel-toe of her boot. It's Bikini Kill's Instant Macho Gun Revolution. A shoot-em-up movie, big engines, sweat. Getting her hands dirty. Or

playing roller derby.

If being an athlete is a feminist act, what is a brawl? Can our bodies be

a striking fist?

We are in control. Practicing love, taking turns absorbing impact, lying

on the ground. Pressing against stratums of ability. Consenting to

disorder. Safe.

It all makes so much sense behind these Barn walls. We are ego and

the altar, life lived outside this space and the life lived within.

Remember violence done to you. Nerve endings lighting up along your

back, pleasure, nails down the insides of your arms. Damp tightening. A

bite.

Pinch. Did you like how it felt? A shove, the ground rushing up to meet

you. Adrenaline vibrating in your chest. Release.

Muscle tissue grates, sinew unbraiding reforming density. It hurts to.

Grow. Scar. There's pain in metamorphosis. Will your body match your

size?

Flesh defined by our movements through others. Neither two nor one.

Identity given and made. Life not only plural, singular.

Suspended in air / eye contact, buckle.

Lex rejects this role as whore or housewife, a toxic dichotomy. Give her

two names (no, three!),

a form like moonlight and stones,

made of love   and making love,

waking life soaked.

In sheets.

Unsatisfied with this lexicon of womanhood.

She shifts shapes and drips thick, like bitten fruit. Here the bend of her

knees is a place of strength, sex may be fist or flower, we are uprooted

at the groin.

She doesn't want to be a boy or a girl, she wants to be a tear. A

perforation. Endlessly stepping out of herself like skippers, hairstreaks,

and swallowtails

fracture a chrysalis. Fluid in desire, a looped life outstretched.

20.

Devil Dan packs his suitcase in the backseat of '08, leaving hot tire

marks in the desert parking lot. Kathleen snarls from a jukebox behind windows of neon cacti and Budweiser ads. Dust is rising, it's time to

disrupt the

(status quo)

Cartridge belts slung low

across hips, boots laced tight, a stubbed out cigarette behind an ear.

Hands in the center, yell, "Texas Texas, kill kill kill!" Welcome to the

culture war. Picked the wrong group of women to two-step.

It's babes beating each other up

yeah, something like that.

Alexa Chrisbacher lives in a Denver attic with her partner, a dog, and a cat. She received her MFA from the Jack Kerouac School of Disembodied Poetics at Naropa University and skates for Denver Roller Derby. This is her first book.

CPSIA information can be obtained
at www.ICGtesting.com
Printed in the USA
LVHW111749160519
618107LV00005B/909/P

9 781732 682764